MW00484228

Printed and bound in the United States of America.

ISBN 0-9709149-0-3

KNACKK PRESS
8733 WEST SUMMIT CIRCLE DRIVE
FRENCH LICK, IN 47432

This lighter look at chemotherapy comes to you from a two-time sufferer under the IV needle. It is meant to bring a laugh, or at least a smile, to those now fighting the fight, and to seasoned veterans as well. Extra pages have been inserted so you can make this book your own. Please personalize it by adding your own hard-won pieces of humor and wisdom.

#1 ~ Doctors actually call you back!

2 ~ You get to live every driver's fantasy:
Park in handicap spaces without being towed.

3 ~ You don't have to tip your barber.

4 ~ Following chemo, you'll feel 10 years younger when you're 3 years older.

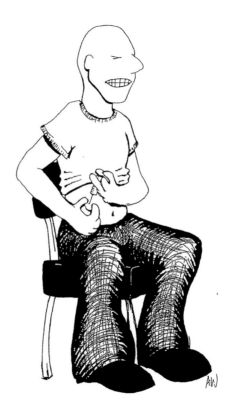

#5 ~ You can become very adept at needling people by practicing on yourself.

6 ~ *You can wow 'em at cocktail parties with your new insider's vocabulary of words like "Peripheral Neuropathy," "Neutropenic" and "Protocol."*

7 ~ Commercials for aspirin and over-the-counter pain relievers will no longer hold you spellbound ~ you will have experienced the big leagues of pain and relief.

8 ~ *You have a valid excuse, and the time (if not maybe the energy) to read the junk fiction you've always wanted to read.*

9 ~ You now have an ice-breaking conversational topic for any social occasion. When someone stares at your missing eyebrows, you can say, "I'm in chemotherapy."

#10 ~ There'll be no need to shave your legs.

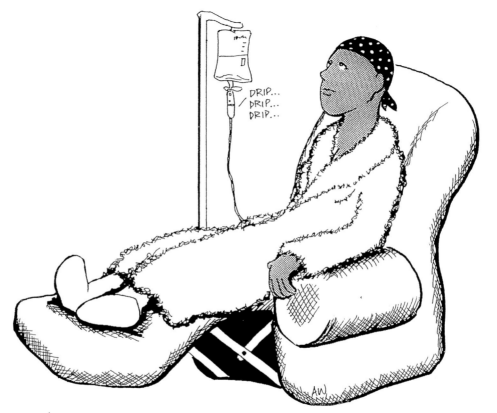

11 ~ The sensation that days are flying by will be replaced by the feeling that certain days (treatment days and the following five, especially) have grown much longer.

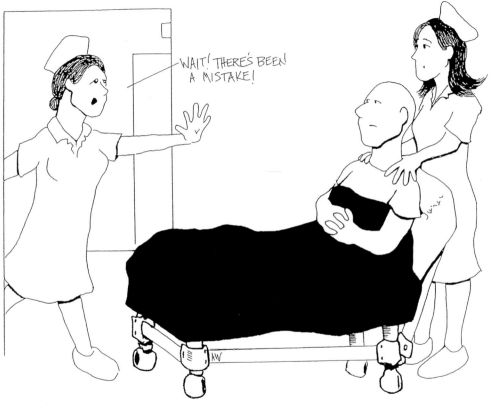

#12 ~ *You'll learn to entrust total strangers with the care and preservation of your life. Conversely, you'll learn why you never trusted total strangers.*

13 ~ *You'll either lose weight and be thin, or, if you're given Prednisone, puff up. In either case, there'll be no messing with Mr. In-between.*

 # 14 ~ You will become a connoisseur of fruit juices, since, at times, nothing else will go or stay down.

15 ~ *Mental confusion provides the perfect excuse for not making decisions.*

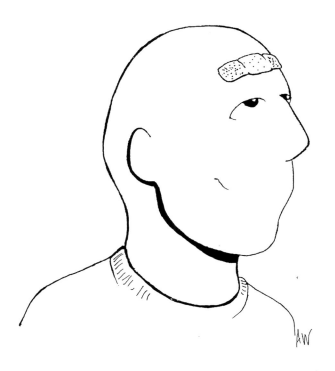

#16 ~ Bandages come off with much less pain.

 # 17 ~ You can take naps without feeling guilty or being accused of laziness.

#18 ~ Hairy underarms are, for awhile, things of the past.

#19 ~ *No more dingleberries!*

20 ~ If you are accustomed to bad cooking, your food will suddenly taste better; it won't taste at all!

 # 21 ~ You'll have the perfect excuse to avoid people you want to avoid.

22 ~ *You'll have the perfect excuse to draw closer to people you want to draw closer to.*

23 ~ You can miss the holiday rush at the hairdresser.

24 ~ There'll be no need to argue with doctors to get pain pills. They'll believe you.

25 ~ *No longer will you be blissfully ignorant of the oh-so-moderate prices of prescription medicine.*

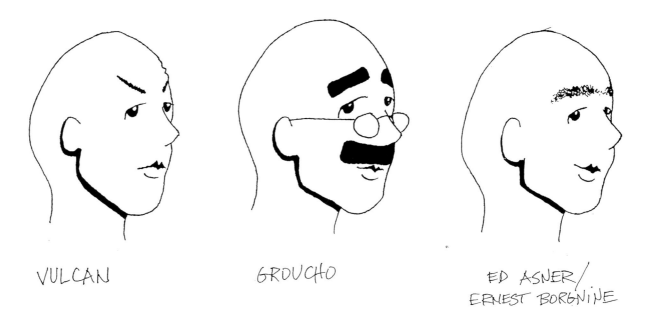

VULCAN   GROUCHO   ED ASNER/
                                 ERNEST BORGNINE

 # 26 ~ You won't need to pluck your eyebrows ~ an eyebrow pencil and a little creativity can produce any number of new looks.

 # 27 ~ Constipation will be a thing of the past.

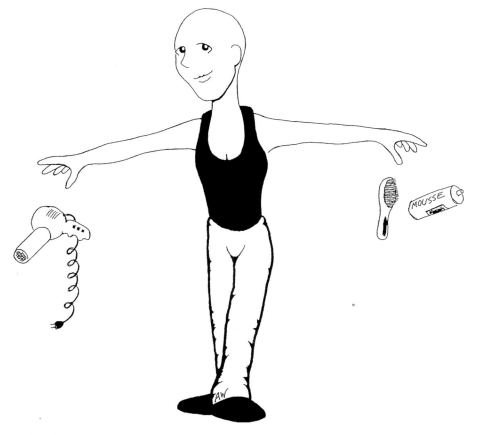

28 ~ You can save a lot of money on hair mousse.

29 ~ Between nerve damage from the drugs and being stuck a thousand times with needles, splinters won't hurt nearly as much as they used to.

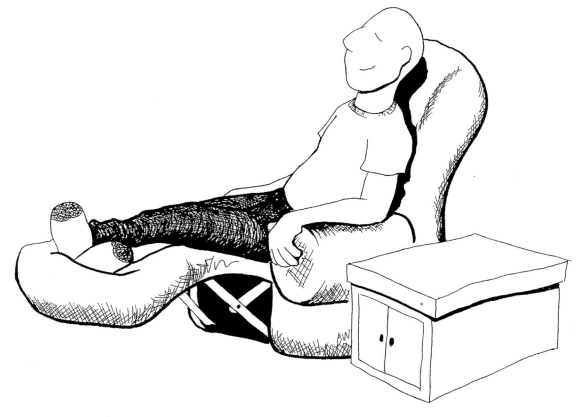

#30 ~ Your entertainment needs will be easily met ~ you'll sleep a lot.

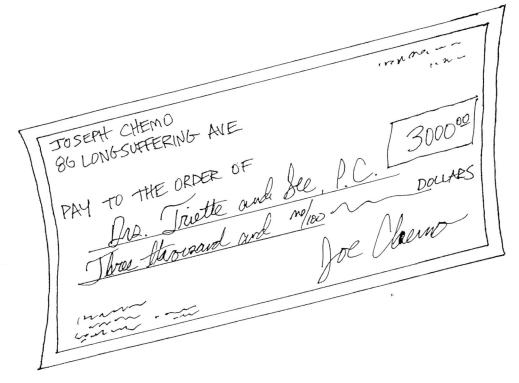

JOSEPH CHEMO
86 LONGSUFFERING AVE

PAY TO THE ORDER OF

Drs. Triette and See, P.C.

$3000.00

Three thousand and no/100 ~~~~~~~~ DOLLARS

Joe Chemo

 # 31 ~ Considering the cost of chemotherapy, you can be proud to be doing your part to keep the economy going.

#32 ~ *No more unsightly ear hairs.*

#33 ~ *Little things, small pleasures, will mean more to you.*

#34 ~ You will learn what good friends and family are all about.

35 ~ The stock you purchased in paper towel and toilet tissue companies should increase substantially.

 # 36 ~ No more shaving nicks.

37 ~ Chemo provides extra incentive to give up coffee, tobacco, wine, beer or anything else you've been enjoying all your life.

 # 38 ~ With peripheral neuropathy (nerve damage), those tight shoes won't seem to pinch so much.

#39 ~ You may not be famous, but you can now claim to be "noded" in your field of endeavor.

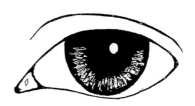

#40 ~ You'll save money on mascara.

41 ~ *You can effortlessly masquerade as the King of Siam, a famous basketball player, or, with the proper color do-rag, a gang member.*

STATE OF CONFUSION

DRIVERS LICENSE ADULT

SEX	HT	WT	HAIR	EYES
M	6'0	VARIES	GONE	BLOODSHOT

EXPIRES:
NOT YET

JOSEPH CHEMO
86 LONGSUFFERING AVE

42 ~ *Chemo taxes the ability of Motor Vehicle personnel to make a driver's license photo look worse than reality.*

43 ~ *You won't be getting hairs caught in your zipper.*

44 ~ *With only your stomach, your throat and a large plastic basin, you can duplicate professional sound effects from the movie, The Exorcist.*

 # 45 ~ The IRS will seem a lot less intimidating after chemotherapy.

46 ~ *Chemo gives you ESP. White cell booster shots let you foresee the future by experiencing what old age and arthritis will feel like.*

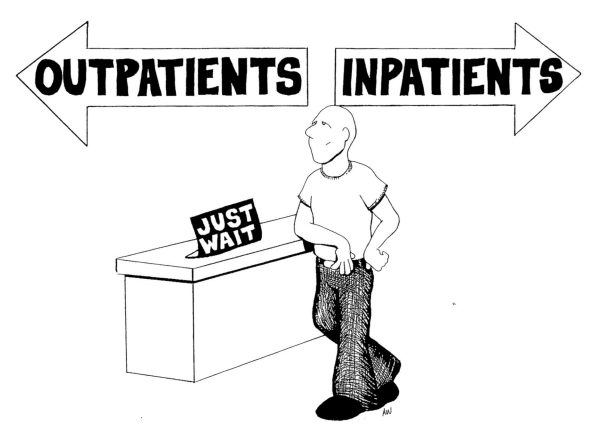

47 ~ You'll learn patience: in-patients, out-patients, and impatience.

48 ~ *If you get off chemotherapy in August, you can enjoy a hairy Christmas. Depending on how the drugs affect you, you could have yourself a very Hairy Christmas.*

#49 ~ *In chemotherapy, all symptoms are "flu-like."*

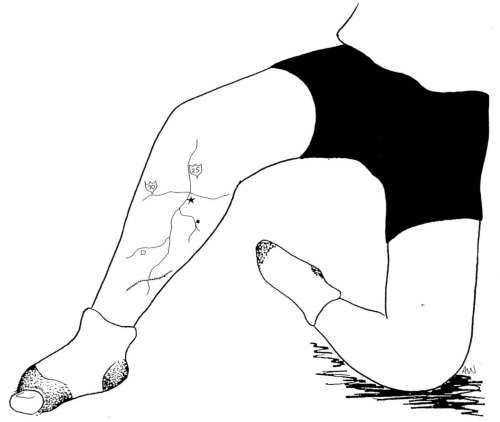

#50 ~ That lone varicose vein that's been worrying you won't be so lonely after chemo wreaks its havoc.

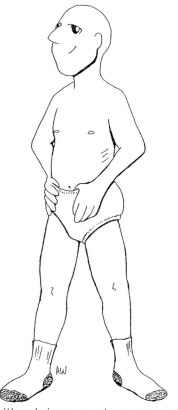

51 ~ *The doctors will advise you to pamper yourself at times . . .*
. . . other brands will work just as well.

#52 ~ Fly-by-night health insurance companies will stop pestering you.

 # 53 ~ Chemo justifies buying a new hat ~ several new hats.

#54 ~ You will never again lack for something to think about, especially when trying to go to sleep.

#55 ~ You have an excuse for lazin' in the shade.

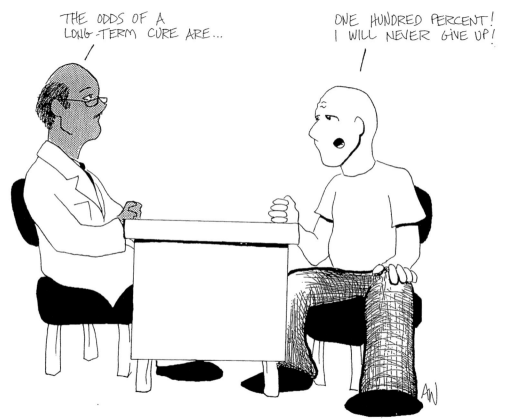

#56 ~ The odds of winning the lottery won't seem so absurd after chemo.

MEGAHEALTH inc.

57 ~ Remember, if you have cancer, you are part of a "growth" industry.